THE EIGHTH WONDER

THE EIGHTH WONDER

B. F. STURTEVANT COMPANY
HYDE PARK · BOSTON, MASS.

First edition, November, 1927
Second edition, January, 1928

THE UNIVERSITY PRESS, CAMBRIDGE MASS.
Printed in U.S.A.

GRATEFUL acknowledgment is made for valuable data obtained from the official reports of the New York and New Jersey Tunnel Commissions and from the *Engineering News Record*, and for permission to reprint a portion of an article from the magazine *Charm*, published by L. Bamberger & Co., Newark, N. J.

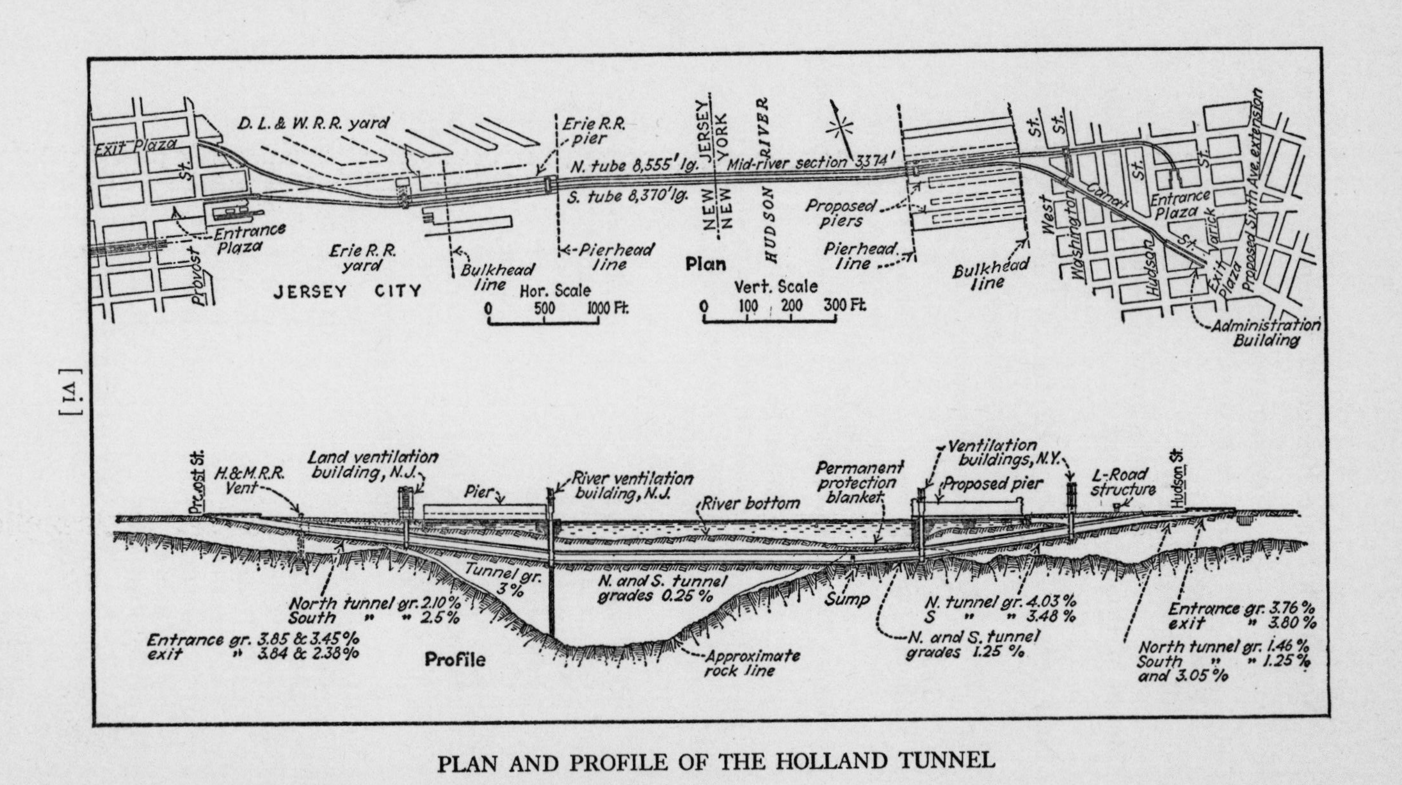

PLAN AND PROFILE OF THE HOLLAND TUNNEL

New York State Bridge & Tunnel Commission

COMMISSIONERS

George R. Dyer, *Chairman*

E. W. Bloomingdale
McDougall Hawkes
A. J. Shamberg
Albert Goldman

Frederick Stuart Greene

Morris M. Frohlich, *Secretary*
Paul Windels, *Counsel*

New Jersey Interstate Bridge & Tunnel Commission

COMMISSIONERS

Theodore Boettger, *Chairman*

Thomas J. S. Barlow
John F. Boyle
Isaac Ferris
John B. Kates
Weller H. Noyes
Robert S. Sinclair

Frank L. Suplee

E. Morgan Barradale, *Secretary*
Robert Carey, *Counsel*

CHIEF ENGINEERS

Clifford M. Holland, 1924
Milton H. Freeman, 1925
Ole Singstad

CONSULTANTS

J. A. Bensel, 1922
George H. Brown
William H. Burr
Edward A. Byrne
C. F. Cahalane
J. Vipond Davies
Henry W. Hodge, 1919
Sullivan W. Jones
Dr. Edward Levy
George L. Lucas
Frederick C. Noble
Lewis B. Stillwell
George L. Watson
William J. Wilgus
Arthur C. Willard
Frank M. Williams

ENGINEERING ASSISTANTS

O. L. Brodie
C. L. Crandall
A. C. Davis
J. N. Dodd
J. H. Dugan
L. Geenens
C. S. Gleim
J. C. Imhoff
A. H. Jorgensen
M. I. Killmer
H. L. King
J. Mechanic
C. W. Murdock
Erling Owre
Ralph Smillie
Jesse B. Snow
Frederic A. Snyder
E. Welle

ILLUSTRATIONS

Facing Page

ILLUSTRATIONS

Facing Page

THE EIGHTH WONDER

I

BACK in the second century B.C., a certain Antipater of Sidon composed an epigram in which he enumerated what he termed the "Seven Wonders of the World." They were the walls of Babylon, the statue at Olympia by Phidias, the hanging gardens at Babylon, the Colossus of Rhodes, the pyramids of Egypt, the mausoleum at Halicarnassus, and the temple of Artemis at Ephesus.

Today any similar list of wonders, no matter by whom compiled, would doubtless include the Pyramids, not merely because they alone have survived the ravages of time, but because they still represent a marvelous achievement of man's handiwork. What the other wonders would be might afford material for a contest sponsored by some newspaper columnist. But surely there would be a place in such a list for the Holland Tunnel, as the longest subaqueous tunnel in the world, a stupendous project, magnificently conceived and executed. And surely old Antipater himself, however wedded he might be to his own wonders, would today be glad to add the Holland Tunnel to his list, as an eighth wonder of the world.

It is with this belief that the following record of its history has been written, in recognition of the magnitude of the task, of the heroism of its first chief engineer, Clifford M. Holland, and his successor, Milton H. Freeman, both of whom gave their lives to the undertaking, and of the great advance in the science of ventilation which its construction made possible.

II

OF course, a tunnel is no new thing. Primitive man, living close to nature, could hardly have failed to observe evidences of tunneling by animal life about him, and soon made tunnels for his own purposes. We know that in ancient Egypt a king, upon ascending the throne, began at once to excavate the long narrow passage leading to the rock-hewn chamber at Thebes which was to be his tomb. From Egypt, too, comes the first record of a subaqueous tunnel — constructed under the dry bed of the river Euphrates, which had been temporarily diverted from its channel. It was 12 feet wide, 15 feet high, and was lined with brick masonry.

In the time of Cæsar Augustus, or perhaps even earlier, the Romans built a notable tunnel through the Posilipo hills between Naples and Pozzuoli, about 3000 feet long and 25 feet wide. In order to light this tunnel, its floor and roof were made to converge gradually from the ends to the middle: at the entrances it was 75 feet high. The Romans were the greatest tunnel builders of antiquity. During the Middle Ages, tunnel building was chiefly for military purposes. Every great castle had its private underground passage from the central tower or keep to some distant concealed place, through which to make sorties, receive supplies, or escape in time of need.

With the advent of gunpowder and of canal construction, a strong impetus was given to tunnel building in its more modern aspect of commercial or public utility. Previous to 1800, canal tunnels were all through rock or hard ground. Then, in 1803, a soft-ground tunnel 24 feet wide was excavated for the Saint Augustine Canal in France. Timbers were laid to support the roof and walls as fast as the earth was removed, and the masonry lining built closely following. From this experience the various systems of soft-ground tunneling since employed have developed.

The use of shield and metal lining marks the greatest development in the art of soft-ground submarine tunneling. The shield was invented and first used by Sir Marc Isambard Brunel in excavating the first tunnel under the river Thames at London, begun in 1825 and opened in 1843. In 1869 Peter William Barlow used an iron lining in connection with a shield in driving the second tunnel under the Thames at London.

The modern tunnel shield is a steel-plate cylinder whose forward edge acts as a cutting edge. Its rear end, extending backward, overlaps the tunnel lining of cast-iron rings. Inside the shield, hydraulic jacks act against the tunnel lining as a thrust block so as to push the shield ahead when pressure is applied. A partition prevents earth from entering the shield except as permitted through suitable openings. As the shield moves forward, the lining is erected under the protection of its rear. In submarine tunneling compressed air pumped into the forward end of the tunnel counter-balances the pressure of the water which tries to enter.

III

IN 1906 the legislatures of the states of New York and New Jersey created for each state a Bridge Commission to investigate the feasibility of constructing a bridge over the Hudson River, uniting New York City with Jersey City. Legislative recognition was thus given to an increasingly vital problem — some means to supplement the ferries plying between these two ports.

Further legislation, enacted from time to time, continued the life of these Commissions. In 1913 they were authorized to consider the possibility of a vehicular tunnel. Finally, on April 10, 1919, authority was granted them to proceed with the construction of a tunnel, or tunnels, between a point in the vicinity of Canal Street on the island of Manhattan and a point in Jersey City.

Those who had the project closest at heart felt that the tunnel would

1. Shorten the time of transit across the Hudson River and afford a continuous means of communication between New York and New Jersey, unaffected by climatic or other interference.
2. Relieve traffic congestion, already serious.
3. Accelerate the movement of necessary supplies into the city of New York, and thereby relieve conditions of distress.
4. Increase the tax value of real property within a considerable radius of the tunnel terminals.
5. Pay its cost three times over within twenty years.
6. Reduce the high cost of living by reducing the cost of trucking.
7. Increase the facilities for commerce in the port of New York by removing from the surface of the harbor many lighters and other floating equipment.

8. Furnish means for the uninterrupted movement of troops and supplies to and from the city of New York in case of need.

The Commissions selected as chief engineer Mr. Clifford M. Holland, tunnel engineer of the Public Service Commission, First District, State of New York, in immediate charge of the construction of all subway tunnels under the East River. He was regarded as having had a greater and more successful experience in the work of subaqueous tunnel construction than any other member of his profession. A board of consulting engineers was appointed, and a contract or treaty between the two states was drawn up and approved by the Commissions and given the consent of Congress.

Chief Engineer Holland took office on July 1, 1919, and at once began the organization of an engineering staff. His chief assistants were selected from those who had been associated with him in the construction of the East River subway tunnels. Having had not less than ten years' experience in subaqueous tunneling, they were well qualified both by technical training and by practical experience to meet the requirements of the work. Actual construction began October 12, 1920.

Upon the death of Mr. Holland on October 27, 1924, at Battle Creek Sanitarium, where he had gone in search of health after devoting all his strength and energy to the construction of the tunnel, the Commissions gave it his name. Under his direction all the more difficult portions had been completed and the remaining details planned, and on the very day his body was borne to his home there came a demonstration of his engineering skill and accuracy in the successful junction of the under-river headings of the north tunnel.

His successor, Mr. Milton H. Freeman, had been his Division Engineer. He, too, gave himself unsparingly to the work, and died on March 24, 1925. He was succeeded by Mr. Ole Singstad, who had been Engineer of Designs under both Mr. Holland and Mr. Freeman. Under his direction the Holland Tunnel has been completed.

CLIFFORD MILBURN HOLLAND

Genius of the Holland Tunnel and its first chief engineer, in memory of whom the tunnel was named

SITE OF THE HOLLAND TUNNEL, LOOKING WEST FROM NEW YORK CITY

IV

THE Holland Tunnel is located in the vicinity of Canal Street, New York City, because that street is a wide east and west thoroughfare giving direct communication across the island of Manhattan. On the east, Canal Street connects with the East River bridges and Brooklyn; on the west, with the Hudson River water front, at approximately the center of down-town traffic over the Hudson ferries.

Its location in Jersey City is at the logical point as nearly opposite Canal Street as is practicable, in order to obtain the shortest tunnel. This point is very near the center of traffic and is advantageously located. It gives direct communication to Jersey City Heights and points beyond by means of the Thirteenth Street Viaduct. The water front, with important railroad yards, is easily accessible and adequate communication is afforded with the low-lying parts of Jersey City and Hoboken through streets which parallel the river.

The southerly tube for eastbound traffic extends from Provost and Twelfth Streets, Jersey City, under the Erie Railroad yards, the Hudson River, and Canal Street to Varick Street, New York City. The northerly tube for westbound traffic extends from Broome Street midway between Varick and Hudson Streets in New York City, curving to the west to Spring and Hudson Streets and under Hudson Street and the Hudson River, the Erie, and the Delaware, Lackawanna and Western Railroad yards to Fourteenth Street at Provost Street, Jersey City.

In planning a public undertaking of the magnitude of the Holland Tunnel, consideration had to be given to many features besides those of actual tunneling. The building of the structure itself was a great engineering problem, but many investigations beyond mere technical design were required.

To secure the best location and arrangement of tunnel roadways, a survey of present and future traffic and the influence of the tunnel on the development of adjacent territory was called for, first of all. Traffic conditions had to be considered from many angles, such as capacity, congestion of the tunnel roadway, adequate approaches, congestion in adjoining streets, width of roadway, and the growth and development of vehicular traffic.

A preliminary forecast of tunnel traffic, based chiefly on the yearly increase in traffic over the Hudson ferries, resulted in an estimate of the number of vehicles that would use the tunnel as follows:

1924 (when tunnel was expected to be opened)	5,610,000
1935	13,800,000
1937	15,700,000
1943	22,300,000

Further estimates indicated that a one-line tunnel would have a capacity about equal to the traffic demand at the opening of the tunnel. A two-line tunnel would have sufficient capacity to accommodate all traffic up to 1937, while a three-line tunnel would reach its capacity in 1943.

Obviously it would be unwise to construct a one-line tunnel whose capacity would be reached as soon as put in operation. As between a two-line and a three-line tunnel, it was found that the difference in cost, with interest, would be sufficient to pay for another two-line tunnel after the first two-line tunnel had outgrown its capacity. Of greater importance was the consideration that no street or section could accommodate the volume of traffic represented by a three-line tunnel.

If a three-line tunnel were built, it could be operated at only two-line capacity. This would violate two of the main principles governing proper tunnel planning — the distribution of traffic so as to avoid undue congestion, and the investment of capital for construction only as facilities are needed, without the necessity of providing for the distant future. These are two of the most important features in which tunnel construction is held to be superior to bridge construction in crossing wide, navigable rivers.

The cost of a long-span bridge does not vary directly with the span but increases about as the square of the span. On such a bridge no commensurate saving in the cost of construction is obtained by omitting some of its facilities. The tendency in bridge construction, therefore, is to provide facilities greatly in excess of immediate requirements, with a consequent expenditure of capital long before those facilities are needed. Then when there is sufficient traffic to utilize the bridge to full capacity, the resulting congestion in the vicinity of the bridge entrances becomes a serious matter. This is seen in the case of the East River bridges in New York City today.

Tunnel construction, on the other hand, is more flexible than bridge construction, because the cost is a direct function of its length, with the volume of excavation increasing as the square of the diameter. Since the cost of excavation represents a large part of the total cost of a tunnel, any increase in the width of roadway can be made only at considerable expense. The proper way to plan a tunnel is to avoid the disadvantages inherent in bridge construction, build only for the present and near future, and construct other tunnels at other locations when the facilities of the first tunnel are outgrown.

Since a two-line tunnel would have sufficient capacity to accommodate traffic up to 1937, and a three-line tunnel would create such traffic congestion in the vicinity of its entrances and exits as to preclude its use to capacity; also since the difference in cost between a two-line and a three-line tunnel, with interest, would pay for a new two-line tunnel when the first was outgrown, the obvious proceeding was to construct a two-line tunnel and when its capacity is reached, to build another two-line tunnel at some other location as determined by future traffic conditions. The Holland Tunnel is, therefore, a twin-tube tunnel, providing in each tube for two lines of traffic in each direction.

In planning the entrances and exits of the tunnel, a careful study was made of vehicular traffic, with particular reference to its movement at street intersections and through the tunnel. It was recognized that wherever traffic intersects, its continuity is broken. Instead of moving in a steady stream, it breaks into a series of waves as it is held up and released at intersections. This interruption in the stream of traffic at street intersections so limits the capacity of a street that its real capacity as determined by its width is never reached.

A tunnel differs from a street in that the only interrup-

SECTIONAL VIEW OF HOLLAND TUNNEL

Under the Hudson River, looking toward New York City

MILTON H. FREEMAN
Who succeeded Mr. Holland as Chief Engineer, and who died in 1925

tions by cross traffic are at the entrances and exits. Consequently these points are of vital importance, affecting as they do the ultimate capacity of the tunnel. Unless the entrances and exits insure continuity of traffic during the period of maximum demand, the capacity of the tunnel roadway can never be reached.

Accordingly, the entrances and exits of the Holland Tunnel are widely separated. In New York City, one is to the north and the other to the south of the Canal Street through traffic; in addition they are located so as to be served by two main north and south avenues. Tunnel traffic is thus given the best possible facility for free movement while at the same time the greatest separation is secured at a reasonable cost. In accord with this same principle the entrance and exit at the Jersey City end are located in separate streets adjacent to the railroad yards east of the north and south traffic streets connecting Jersey City with Hoboken.

This separation of the tunnel entrance and exit traffic is considered to be a factor of the greatest importance in relieving congestion in the vicinity of the tunnel. This was particularly necessary in New York City, with its large and rapidly increasing volume of traffic. It was also called for in Jersey City, where there were no wide thoroughfares in the vicinity of the tunnel.

In addition, property was taken to provide broad plazas at entrances and exits. The entrance plazas serve to accommodate the waves of traffic as they approach the tunnel and converge in the portal roadway into continuous lines of vehicles through the tunnel. Similarly wide exit plazas insure the free and uninterrupted movement of traffic away from the tunnel. Through the separation of entrance from exit, and the use of adequate plazas, the tunnel traffic can be distributed over a large number of streets.

In considering the requirements for the width of the roadways and the clear headroom needed, measurements were taken of vehicles crossing the Hudson on the ferries between New York and New Jersey. It was found that their height varied from 6 feet 6 inches for passenger cars to a maximum of 13 feet for large loaded trucks, but that the number exceeding 12 feet in height was only 1%. The width of motor vehicles varied from 6 feet for passenger cars and light trucks to a maximum of 10 feet 6 inches for army transport trucks. In the case of three-horse teams, the outside dimension of the three horses abreast was 9 feet, but the number of vehicles exceeding 8 feet in width was only 3½%.

In determining the amount of clear headroom required, it was necessary to consider the matter of providing sufficient area in the tunnel roadway. Any increase in clear headroom, without increasing the size of the tunnel, could be made only at the expense of the available ventilating duct area. Any reduction in this area would increase the power required for ventilation and add to the cost of operating the tunnel.

Given a maximum height of 12 feet 2 inches and a maximum width of 8 feet, a clear headroom of 13 feet 6 inches seemed adequate to allow even for jacking up vehicles in case of breakdown, and this was decided upon.

Normal operating conditions in a tunnel accommodating two lines of vehicles in the same direction on one roadway obtain when there is a slow line of heavy trucks 8 feet wide abreast of a fast line of light trucks and passenger cars 6 feet wide. It is, however, necessary to provide for such a contingency as when a vehicle of maximum width has to pass another of the same width that has stalled. The roadway has to be sufficiently wide to permit the passage abreast of two vehicles of maximum width.

It was believed that in the slow line, operating at a speed varying from 3 to 6 miles per hour, a clearance of not less than 6 feet between the outside of the tire and the curb should be provided. In the fast line, due to the greater speed, this clearance should not be less than 1 foot. It was also considered that for safe and convenient operation a clearance between moving vehicles of 2 feet 9 inches should be allowed. These considerations led to the adoption of a width of roadway of 20 feet, with, in addition, a sidewalk 2 feet wide in each tunnel. This sidewalk is set back from the curb line a distance of 6 inches and is located at an elevation of 26 inches above the roadway.

This roadway is paved with granite blocks laid in the usual sand cement cushion layer, about one inch thick, with the joints filled with hot asphalt mixed with heated sand. By means of squeegees, a thin coating, sprinkled with sand, is left upon the surface, resulting in a smooth, resilient, and long-wearing surface that will help to deaden the sounds due to traffic, and be more quickly repaired than concrete.

Each side of the roadway is lined with a granite curb, the roadway having a transverse slope from one side to the other, with a depressed concrete gutter behind the curbstone on the low side with side inlet openings at frequent intervals. The drain connects with a sump at the low point of the tunnel, from which a discharge pipe is carried under the roadway of each tunnel to the New York river shaft. Intercepting sumps with pumping equipment are provided in all the river and land shafts.

The tunnel is lighted by electric lamps located in the side walls of the tunnel immediately below the ceiling slabs. A continuous water main is provided throughout the entire length of each tube, with hose connections for fire protection and flushing at frequent intervals.

The walls are lined with white tile, care being taken to eliminate all tile containing blue, green, or red tints, upon advice of a "color psychologist," on account of its "depressing effects." The color of the borders is a light orange. The ceiling is painted white.

The tunnel, with its twin tubes, 29 feet 6 inches in diameter, is the largest subaqueous tunnel in America, exceeding by 6 feet 6 inches the Pennsylvania Railroad tubes. On the New Jersey side, the diameter of one of the tubes is increased to 30 feet 4 inches to meet ventilation requirements. This exceeds by 4 inches the diameter of the Rotherhithe Tunnel under the river Thames, London, England, which has been the largest subaqueous tunnel in the world.

HOLLAND TUNNEL AND HUDSON AND MANHATTAN R.R. TUNNEL

Full-sized section of Holland Tunnel (diameter 29′ 6″) and full-sized section of Hudson and Manhattan R.R. Tunnel (diameter 16′ 7″)
Rings weigh 16,630 pounds and 5670 pounds per linear foot, respectively

ASSEMBLING SHIELD IN CANAL STREET SHAFT
View looking down into shaft, showing bulkhead in west side wall

V

THE shield method of construction was adopted for the Holland Tunnel after careful consideration of other schemes, notably the trench method. By the trench method, the work is conducted from a plant floating in the river, and the tunnel is constructed either under a protecting roof or floated into position and sunk in sections in a dredged trench. The longest subaqueous tunnel built by this method is the Detroit River tunnel of the Michigan Central Railroad.

It was recognized that in the excavation of a trench under the Hudson River, there would be an unavoidable interference with a great volume of river traffic. Fifteen hundred boats cross the line of the tunnel daily. Such congested river conditions would make every dredge or other machine working in the tunnel an obstruction to traffic. Collisions would be frequent, increasing the time and cost of the work, with danger both to shipping and to the equipment of construction. Storms, fog, and ice would cause a discontinuance of surface work for at least two months of each year. At the New York end, a large mass of ledge rock, involving blasting and removal at great depth, would be a serious obstacle to open trench excavation under water.

Since there was a real hazard involved in carrying on operations from a plant anchored in mid-stream, the shield method was clearly called for. In addition, silt conditions in the Hudson River were regarded as extremely favorable to this method. In a trench tunnel, soft material greatly increases the volume of excavation, while in the case of a shield tunnel this material is most easily excavated. If the silt is not shoved aside by the shields, it is easily disposed of through the tunnel. The shield may be closed with the exception of certain openings through which the material is squeezed into the tunnel as the shield advances.

The first contract provided for the sinking of two land shafts, one at Washington and Canal Streets and the other at Washington and Spring Streets, New York City. They were sunk by the compressed-air method.

The double steel walls of the caissons were filled with concrete as the caissons were sunk. This added to their weight when sinking weight was needed, and at the same time completed the structure of the walls. In addition to this concrete, weight for sinking was obtained by storing the excavated material from the working chamber on the roof of the chamber as the caisson went down. This necessitated handling the material a second time, but gave the desired weight and permitted the lowering of the caisson without greatly reducing the air pressure in the working chamber, thereby preventing loss of ground.

Upon the removal of the compressed air, the bottom seals of the caissons proved to be water-tight. The shafts were now ready for the building of the shields preparatory to the beginning of shield tunneling. Temporary bulkheads were provided in the west side walls to permit the passage of the shields, and in the east side walls to connect with the approach section which was to be constructed by excavation from the surface.

This work was followed by placing under contract the entire under-river portion of the tunnel. Power plants had

LAND SHAFT CAISSON AT SPRING STREET, NEW YORK CITY
Showing steel bulkhead in west side wall through which shield advanced after erection

SHIELD, SOUTH TUNNEL, CANAL STREET AT WEST STREET, NEW YORK CITY

View of rear end of shield in place and temporary bulkhead. Tunneling operations temporarily suspended and air pressure removed in order to remove shaft deck and place cages in shaft and air locks in tunnel to be constructed to produce low-pressure air for caissons and tunnel, high-pressure air for the operation of grouting machines, air drills, and hoisting engines used below the surface, and hydraulic pressure for operating the jacks used in driving the shield and for operating the erector arm for building the tunnel lining.

Overhead gantries and dumping platforms for the receipt and disposal of materials and buildings for housing the workmen had to be provided. Pipes, through which compressed air would be supplied to the tunnel headings, had to be laid to the shafts. On the New Jersey side this involved laying low-pressure lines as large as 16 inches in diameter, high-pressure lines, hydraulic lines, water lines, electric cables, and telephone cables. Every facility had to be provided, even an independent telephone system connecting all parts of the work with the public telephone system.

Canal Street Park was made available as a site for the air-compressing plant and engineers' field office. Pier 35 and adjacent slips were used for the storage of materials and for the disposal of excavated matter from the tunnel heading. Overhead gantries connecting the shafts with the pier permitted traffic to the water front in connection with the tunnel to pass above the city streets.

The first shield was erected in the Canal Street shaft. On October 26, 1922, compressed air was introduced into the shield chamber, and tunneling was begun. Each shield was 30 feet 2 inches in outside diameter, 16 feet 4 inches long, and the upper half was equipped with a hood projecting 2 feet 6 inches ahead of the shield proper. Five vertical and three horizontal walls divided the shield into 13 compartments, through which the ground in front was excavated. It was equipped with thirty 10-inch jacks, having a combined thrust of 6000 tons. A hydraulic erector was used to build the tunnel segments into a complete ring. The weight of the shield, with all equipment, was about 400 tons.

The tunnel lining is composed of rings 2 feet 6 inches wide, consisting of 14 segments, each approximately 6 feet long, with a key one foot long, bolted together. Inside the lining is an inner lining of concrete 19 inches thick. As the shield advanced and the lining was erected behind it, the space due to the difference in the diameter of the shield and the rings forming the lining was filled by forcing a grout of cement and sand in equal parts into the void under high air pressure. For this purpose each segment was provided with a grout hole fitted with a screw plug. The lining was made water-tight by placing hemp grommets soaked in red lead around the bolts, and by caulking lead wire into grooves between the segments.

Shield driving requires extreme care and exactitude to keep to line and grade. The position of the shield fixes the location of the tunnel, and no correction can be made afterward. It is absolutely essential that the slightest deviation of the shield from its theoretically correct position be known at once, so that measures may be taken to remedy the error during the next shove. The shield is guided by the operation of the jacks distributed around its circumference, omitting the use of those jacks in the direction toward which the shield is to move.

Every precaution was taken to provide for the safety of the workmen in the compressed-air chambers. A high emergency gangway in the upper part of the tunnel led from the shield to the locks, for escape in case of a blow-out. Safety screens were installed to trap the inrushing water. Fire lines were installed in the compressed-air chambers. Fire is a real danger in compressed-air work on account of the increased amount of oxygen present. As an indication of the fire hazard, a candle, if still glowing when extinguished, will again burst into flame.

The starting of the shields out of the caissons at the New York land shafts was difficult because of the large diameter of the shields and the shallow cover overhead. The material at this point was granular, consisting largely of fine sand, which if undisturbed, held air fairly well. As the shields were under the city streets, it was impossible to increase the cover overhead. To avoid blow-outs at the face with the consequent inrush of water, it was necessary to regulate the air pressure carefully and to protect the face during each successive step in excavating.

As a preliminary step to shoving the shields out of the caissons, the circular steel bulkheads in the caissons were burned out in front of the shields. The work was done by removing the steel in horizontal layers, each layer carefully protected as the steel was removed to avoid exposing a great area of the face to air leakage, especially when the air pressure sufficient to dry out the bottom would be heavy enough to cause a blow-out at the top.

Removal of the steel bulkhead was started, with the steel above intact and with air pressure sufficient to dry out the bottom. After the lower third of the steel bulkhead had been removed, a wooden bulkhead was built in front of the shield, and the space between this bulkhead and the ground ahead was packed with clay. The air pressure was then reduced until it balanced the water pressure at the top of the shield, and work was begun at the top, removing the top plates and proceeding downward.

As these plates were removed, breast boards packed front and back with clay were inserted to cover the exposed excavation. This work proceeded down to the point where the bottom plates had previously been removed, while at the same time the air pressure was raised step by step to balance the water pressure. The shield was then advanced against the wooden bulkhead at the bottom, compressing the clay which was removed as the shield advanced, with the jacks reacting against the cast-iron tunnel lining temporarily erected in the shaft.

In order to prevent the leakage of air around the hood of the shield, an annular pocket was excavated ahead of the hood the full length of a shove, and this pocket was packed with clay. This served a double purpose: first, the hood, as the shield advanced, cut into this clay and made a thorough seal in front against air leakage; and second, by exploring the full length of the shove, assurance was had that the shield would not pick up and drag timbers in front of it, leaving open channels behind them through which air could readily escape. The necessity of taking this precaution is evident when it is considered that at this point there were but 14 feet of cover above the shield to the street surface, and only 8 feet from the top of the shield to the under side of an old brick sewer, which would readily allow the air to escape from the tunnel heading.

As the tail of the shield left the caisson, grouting was at once started to fill the annular space which the shield left

GANG OF "SAND HOGS" IN LINE
Waiting to check in for work in compressed air. Canal Street land shaft and air locks, South Tunnel

HAULING A CAR OF MUCK OUT OF A MUCK LOCK, SOUTH TUNNEL

CONCRETE ROADWAY

Beginning of sidewalk, and reinforcing of sidewalk, North Tunnel. View shows construction track on roadway and roof rebolting and caulking platform

CONCRETE BULKHEAD AND LOCKS

South Tunnel, Canal Street, New York City

outside the tunnel lining. Every effort was made to keep this space fully grouted, even to the extent of stopping the shield in the middle of a shove to keep the grout up with the shield.

The method just described was later modified so that in the bottom quarter of the shield, instead of packing ahead with clay, a fixed wooden bulkhead was built in the shield, and the shield was advanced into the fine wet sand with this bulkhead in place. This compressed the earth, driving out the water, so that the material was firm and could be excavated during the shove over the top of the bulkhead, or through small openings cut in the bulkhead itself. This prevented a free run of wet material into the bottom which is the ordinary method of tunneling under the river.

The grouting previously described was continued, and not only prevented an abnormal escape of air at the tail of the shield, but also prevented settlement of the streets and adjacent buildings. The buildings at the corner of West and Spring Streets settled slightly, but at no time were they in need of shoring, nor were the occupants disturbed at any period of the tunnel work. This was the situation also with the New York Central tracks under which the Canal Street tunnel was driven. The grouting was carried on so effectively that it filled some of the old sewers in the vicinity which later had to be cleaned out.

The Canal Street shield passed very close to a cofferdam around an excavation for a sewage treatment plant, and it was evident from the first that great care must be exercised in driving the tunnel past this location. At the nearest point the shield was within 5 feet of the steel sheeting of the cofferdam, with the bottom of the sheeting at about the springing line of tunnel. On November 30th, when the shield was about 40 feet away, it was noticed that sand and water were being forced through the sheeting into the cofferdam by the air pressure from the tunnel heading. In about two hours approximately 150 cubic yards of earth had been blown into the excavation from behind the sheeting, and it was plain that not only was the cofferdam in danger, but the continuation of tunneling operations would be hazardous because the cavities left in the ground provided open channels for the leakage of air, which might have resulted in a tunnel blow-out. It was decided that tunneling operations should be temporarily suspended, that the steel sheeting of the cofferdam should be left in place permanently, and the concrete walls of the permanent structure placed immediately, being increased in thickness to enable them to withstand the pressure from tunneling operations.

Preparatory to tunneling under the river bulkhead, clay and other material to prevent the escape of the compressed air from the tunnel were deposited in the slip between the piers and on the landward side of the river bulkhead to fill such voids as might remain around the tops of the piles supporting the timber platform of the bulkhead construction. Not only were the voids around the piles filled, but the soft mud in the slip was displaced by the heavier clay, a firmer material and better adapted to resist air leakage.

In this section great care was taken in excavating ahead of the hood to be sure that all piles within the area of the tunnel section were cut off before coming in contact with the shields. This was done to avoid pushing the piles through the ground and leaving back of them an open channel for air to escape. These piles extended down to the springing line of the tunnel excavation, and as many as thirty had to be cut off at one time in advancing the shield the length of one ring. In this manner both shields passed under the river bulkhead without accident.

The tunnels then entered the Hudson River silt. The front of the shield was completely bulkheaded. Some of the lower pockets in the shield were opened to allow a part of the material to enter the tunnel as the shield was advanced. The balance of the material in excavation was displaced bodily. At once it was noticed that there was a tendency for the tunnel lining to rise behind the shield. This rising always accompanied movement of the shield; whenever the shield was stopped the rising ceased. The difficult feature at this point was that the shield was so heavy that it settled while the cast-iron tunnel lining behind the shield rose, so that the shield at all times was below grade while the tunnel lining a short distance back was above grade.

The bulkheads in the shield were moved forward to reduce weight by lessening the amount of muck in the shield. This aided somewhat in keeping the shield from settling and then more material could be taken in through the shield. This procedure lessened the pressure on the tunnel behind and reduced its tendency to rise. As the contract required that a second tunnel bulkhead should be constructed in this vicinity, the south shield was stopped after passing through 218 feet of silt and the bulkhead was built. This bulkhead, which is typical of all the bulkheads, is a concrete wall 10 feet thick, equipped with the usual muck, man and emergency locks, and adds temporarily considerable weight to the tunnel.

With this additional weight, the rising of the tunnel was somewhat checked and after tunneling a distance of 121 feet farther in the silt the shield entered at the bottom of the sand layer which overlies the rock, and thereupon all rising of the completed tunnel during shield driving ceased. In the north tunnel, which was driven through the same material after the south tunnel was built, a larger amount of material was taken in through the shield at the start, and while there was some rising of this tunnel behind the shield, it was very much less than in the south tunnel. In neither tunnel was the movement sufficient to endanger the structure.

The excavation in the part-earth and part-rock section just east of the New York river shaft caisson was carried on by driving a short bottom heading in advance of the shield, in which was placed a concrete cradle with steel rails embedded in it upon which the shield slid. After placing the cradle the rock was blasted out for one or two advances of the shield and then the soft material on top was carefully excavated and supported by poling and breast boards.

The New York river ventilating shaft caisson was sunk by the compressed air method in the river near the New York pierhead line. It was built on launching ways, then launched and drydocked. After concrete had been placed in the pockets surrounding the working chamber, additional steel was erected, carrying it to a height of 55 feet.

A platform supported on piles had been built on three sides of the site (the south side being open ready to receive

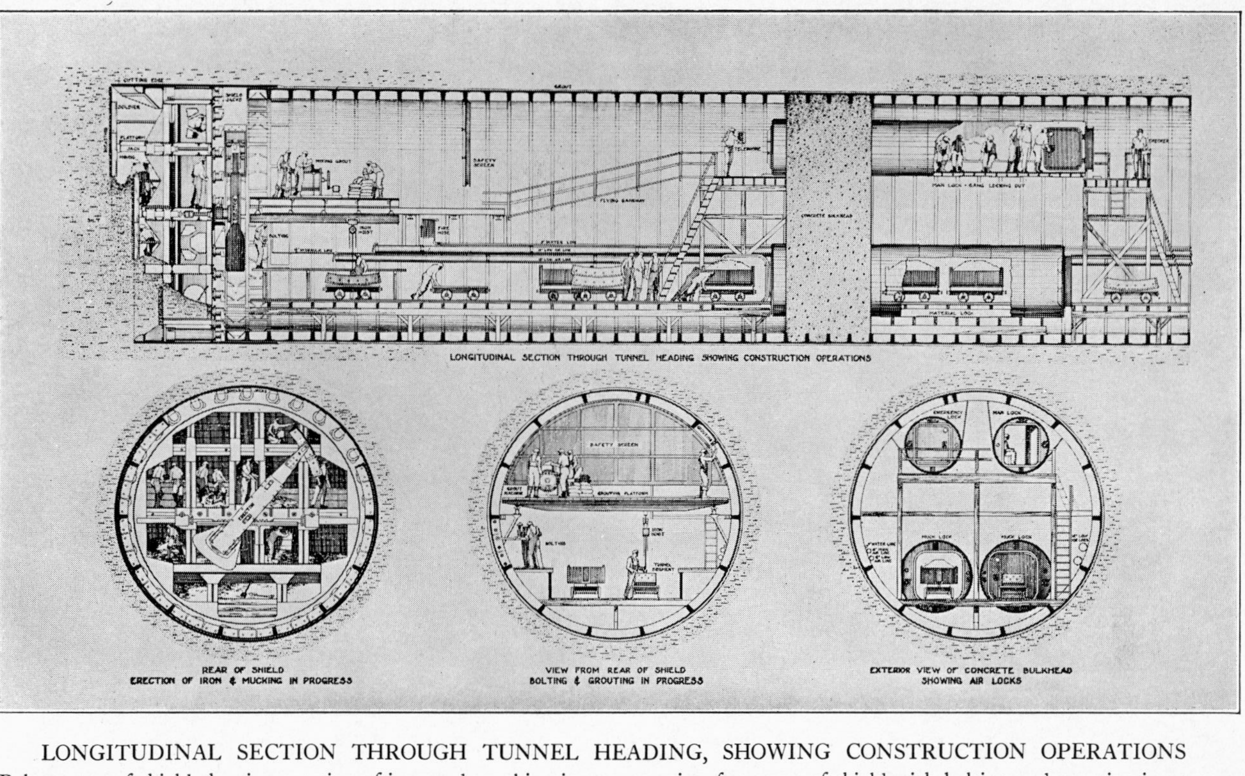

LONGITUDINAL SECTION THROUGH TUNNEL HEADING, SHOWING CONSTRUCTION OPERATIONS

Below, rear of shield showing erection of iron and mucking in process; view from rear of shield with bolting and grouting in process; exterior view of concrete bulkhead showing air locks

NEW JERSEY RIVER SHAFT CAISSON, JUST AFTER LEAVING THE WAYS

Caisson launched at Mariner's Harbor, Long Island, floated into position and sunk

the caisson), and the caisson was towed to its position on the work. The caisson at that time weighed approximately 1650 tons. Upon arrival, additional steel was erected and concrete was placed in the walls, the caisson sinking as the additional weight was placed. Care was taken to keep the center of gravity as low as possible to maintain the necessary stability. When it had reached a depth of 35 feet, the cutting edge encountered the river bottom, into which it settled at each low tide, and weight was added with sufficient rapidity to overcome the tendency to float on the subsequent rising tide.

No excavation was carried on in the working chamber until the cutting edge had penetrated about 9 feet into the mud, as the weight of the caisson displaced the material up to this point. Compressed air was then introduced into the working chamber and the usual shaft mucking operations started. At a depth of 69 feet below mean high water, rock was encountered. This was taken out in lifts about 6 feet deep and the caisson was lowered by successive drops until it reached its final position.

The upper half of the outside of the caisson, or the part which is exposed to open water, was covered with waterproofing, which in turn was covered with an 18-inch layer of protection concrete. An additional protection is afforded in the upper portion by a granite facing where the shaft is exposed to tidal action.

After the caisson was sealed to the rock and waterproof, the east and west shield bulkheads in both the North and South Tunnel chambers were burned out and both shields were driven through the caisson. A timber and concrete cradle of sufficient strength to carry the shield was erected in each chamber and the shield jacked across. After the shields had progressed a sufficient distance west of the river shaft to permit tunnel bulkheads, these were built in each tunnel and placed in operation. After this, tunneling operations were carried on from the river shaft, releasing the tunnels between the land and river shafts for the placing of concrete lining.

VI

THE caissons for the north and south land shafts on the New Jersey side were assembled and sinking started in the fall of 1922. After the caissons had passed through the cinder fill of the railroad yard, a timbercrib filled with riprap was encountered which made excavation extremely difficult. The timbers had to be sawed or chopped into short lengths and some of the rock broken up.

The distance between the tubes on the New Jersey side required the sinking of two separate river ventilating shafts. This presented a problem due to depth of the bedrock, 250 feet as compared with 70 feet on the New York side. It was considered that the silt which overlies the bedrock would not afford a satisfactory support.

Accordingly, it was decided to support the shafts by means of steel casings 24 inches in diameter, filled with reinforced concrete, extending from the bottom of the shafts to ledge rock. They were made in lengths of 20 feet, threaded at both ends for couplings. Three lengths were connected and one end lowered into the silt. The silt inside the pipe was then loosened by churning with a 2000 pound bit, and the mud and water bailed out. Excavation was continued in this manner to a depth of approximately 20 feet below the bottom of the pipe. The material was firm enough to prevent caving into the hold. Another section of pipe was then added and the entire section driven into the hole previously excavated.

The north tunnel shield east and the south tunnel shield

west were built first and started out from their respective caissons. After the south tunnel shield west had progressed a sufficient distance to erect a tunnel bulkhead, the face of the shield was bulkheaded and the roof was removed from the south caisson and the south tunnel shield east was erected. As soon as this shield was ready, the roof was replaced on the caisson and the shield was started eastward, so that at the close of 1923 two shields were tunneling eastward, and one westward.

The method followed in starting these shields out of the shafts was similar to that already described for the New York shields, except that here it was not so difficult as there was adequate cover overhead. After the roof of the working chamber had been replaced, the girders in the side of the caisson, through which the shield was to be advanced, were burned out, after which the plates were removed from the invert to the springing line. The lower pockets of the shield were then bulkheaded and the space between the pockets and the exposed face was filled with clay. After this, the remaining plates were removed, proceeding upward from the springing line. A semicircular annular ring was cleared for the hood and packed with clay into which the hood was forced when the shield was advanced.

The material at the face consisted of timber and riprap down to the springing line, similar to the material encountered in shaft sinking, making excavation very difficult. The stones in the crib varied from one-man stones to those three-quarters of a yard in size. The voids between the stones were filled with soft black mud, which did not offer sufficient resistance to prevent the escape of air,

TIGHTENING BOLTS IN TUNNEL LINING, NORTH TUNNEL

By means of ratchet wrench. Each bolt weighs ten pounds

ERECTOR ARM
Swinging iron segment into place in tunnel lining, South Tunnel, New York City

necessitating the mudding up of the entire face with clay. As the excavation was carried forward, the escape of air through the heading of the north tunnel at times taxed the full capacity of the power house, 40,000 cubic feet of free air per minute.

On June 10, 1923, a small blow occurred at the face of the shield and it became necessary to drop the air pressure sufficiently to allow the water to flow into the tunnel before the blow could be stopped. The progress through the riprap was very slow, as extreme measures had to be taken to avoid blow-outs. After the shield had passed through the old timber and riprap crib, the river bulkhead was encountered which did not offer any unusual difficulties.

Before tunneling through similar material in the south tunnel east, 5500 bags of 1 : 1 Portland cement grout were ejected through the east shield bulkhead of the south caisson and six pipes were sunk from the surface east of the caisson through which 140 bags of 1 : 1 Portland cement grout were placed. This grout displaced much of the soft mud and filled the voids in the riprap and greatly facilitated the driving of the shield so that very little air escaped through this material after it had been consolidated by grouting.

After about sixty rings were erected in each tunnel, the shields were stopped to build tunnel bulkheads and to install cages at the shafts and then tunneling was resumed. Immediately east of the river bulkhead soft mud, considerably lighter than Hudson River silt, was encountered in the upper part of the excavation. In this material the tunnel began to rise directly behind the shield and also to move northward.

To hold the shield and the tunnel to the proper grade, it was necessary to take in a certain amount of material through the shield. Accordingly, the shield was advanced with the top pockets bulkheaded and a large percentage of the excavation was permitted to enter the tunnel through openings in the lower part of the shield. This material had to be entirely removed after each shove before the erection of the cast-iron lining could proceed and slowed down progress. In addition it was desired to retain this material in the tunnel directly behind the shield so as to increase the weight of the tunnel and reduce the tendency to rise.

To meet this situation a different method of tunneling was adopted. The work was stopped and a steel bulkhead semicircular in shape and fitting into the lower part of the tunnel was built to trail about 10 feet behind the shield, and the four pockets of the shield immediately above the springing line were equipped with hydraulically operated doors. When the shield advanced, these doors were opened varying amounts, depending upon conditions, to allow the material to flow through the shield into chutes which cropped the silt back of the trailing bulkhead. This method of tunneling permitted both the shield and the tunnel to be kept on grade.

River-shaft caissons were built, launched, floated into position, and sunk, as on the New York side.

On October 22, 1924, shield driving was suspended in the North Tunnel from the New York side and a bottom heading or junction drift was started to meet a corresponding drift from the New Jersey heading. On October 29, the rock barrier remaining between these headings was blasted away. After this all tunneling operations were

HOLING THROUGH!

Tunnel superintendent Harry Redwood, of New York side, shaking hands with Norman Redwood, of New Jersey side, North Tunnel

CURVE IN SOUTH TUNNEL UNDER WEST STREET, NEW YORK CITY (RADIUS 1000 FEET)
Showing completed rings of cast-iron lining

conducted from the New York side, as the junction was much nearer the New York shaft. The South Tunnel headings were joined on December 7, 1924. Work on the New York side was suspended and the New Jersey shield driven to meet the New York shield.

In July, 1924, the placing of the concrete lining forming the roadway and air ducts was started on the New York side in the North and South Tunnels between the land and river shafts. The concrete invert was first placed in both tunnels from the land shafts to the river shafts. The remaining concrete was then poured in nine operations. Five types of collapsible steel forms in 60-foot sections, afterward increased to 75 feet, supported and moved by carriages resting on previously placed concrete, were used.

The approach tunnels from the land shafts to the open approaches at Dominick and Hudson Streets, New York City, and at Provost Street, Jersey City, were built by the cut and cover method as usually employed in subway construction.

VII

A VISITOR to the Holland Tunnel in 1924 has written the following graphic and interesting story of the shield method of construction. The invitation to inspect the tunnel read, "Wear old clothes and bring your galoshes" —

Such was the admonition of our host on a warm September evening in 1924. But knowing our host, we complied without ado other than a casual lifting of the eyebrows. Ten o'clock that evening found four of us being piloted toward Canal Street and the administration building of the Vehicular Tunnel.

Chief Engineer Holland himself greeted us, and began an introduction to this vast engineering project with maps, diagrams, and more maps and diagrams, till red lines showing tunnels, and blue lines showing traffic lanes, and green lines showing river bed swam before our gaze. We nodded very knowingly, mumbled pleasantly that exquisite shades had been chosen for the various lines, and moved on to the doctor's office.

Here we were introduced to the necessary procedure before going into compressed-air chambers. Ears, heart, and blood pressure were examined. As we were found physically fit, we were passed on to the wardrobe, where we were presented with an assortment of khaki coveralls and left to our own discretion as to choice.

The first twinge of squeamishness about cleanliness was quickly dispelled by the romantic second thought that the very men who were performing this miracle under the river had worn these selfsame garments. Then followed a scramble for the most bespattered on the theory that such muck was a mark of courage in dashing into subaqueous passages. Size was completely disregarded. Never in all the stages of dressing-up to set forth for adventure in my childhood days had I enjoyed more of a thrill as so arrayed we followed our guides to the tunnel entrance.

Once inside we were amazed to find what a simple form such a complex sounding work could assume. The tubes are made of cast-iron segments bolted together. Fourteen of these sections are required to make a complete ring. Each section weighs one and one-half tons and is held in place by huge bolts weighing ten pounds.

"Oh's" and "Ah's" were vented as we continued our way to see the actual excavating. We passed groups of men sitting about talking, laughing, and playing cards, awaiting their shifts. Work was never stopped twenty-four hours a day, seven days a week. (With a forty-two million dollar investment it was imperative that no time be lost.) We met car after car of excavated material on its way down the temporary tracks to the entrance and out to be dumped.

At last we arrived at the great concrete bulkhead that sealed the compressed-air section, separating it from the completed portion of the tunnel.

The bulkhead contained four air chambers or locks. Two large compartments at the bottom of the bulkhead were equipped with tracks for bringing supplies to the workers and for removing the excavated material. Two smaller chambers were provided in the upper section for the workmen who on entering and leaving the tunnel must be gradually brought from one pressure to another.

We entered one of these (only one was used normally, the other reserved for emergencies) and saw the iron door clanged to and fastened. Then followed lessons in equalizing the pressure inside and outside the head by holding the nose and "snorting" — very much as one does when trying to expel water from the nose after diving. The danger of the "caving in" of one's eardrums was stressed, and we were warned to hold up our hand the moment the pressure became too severe. This was the only way to attract the attention of the man who turned on the compressed air, as the noise made even shouting inaudible.

We sat wild-eyed — expecting the hideous monster to leap upon us any minute. The bark was worse than the bite. Twice we raised our hands and the pressure was turned off until the pressure in our ears was relieved. When the twenty-nine pound mark was reached the door leading into the high-pressure section was opened, and there we were in the very midst of the digging.

Once accustomed to the pressure, it was not noticeable, and we began a siege of questions about the actual excavating.

This work was done under a shield, or movable head, slightly larger than the external diameter of the tunnel. The shield was forced forward two and a half feet at a time, the width of a section, by means of thirty hydraulic jacks supported against the end of the tunnel already built. Several of the jacks were then removed and a segment was hoisted into place by a tremendous erector arm till a complete ring had been added, and then the shield was forced ahead again. Doors in the lower part of the shield allowed about thirty per cent of the

CONCRETE CONSTRUCTION IN SOUTH TUNNEL

Showing a typical cross-section of concrete lining and details. The upper and lower arcs of the tunnel form the ventilating ducts

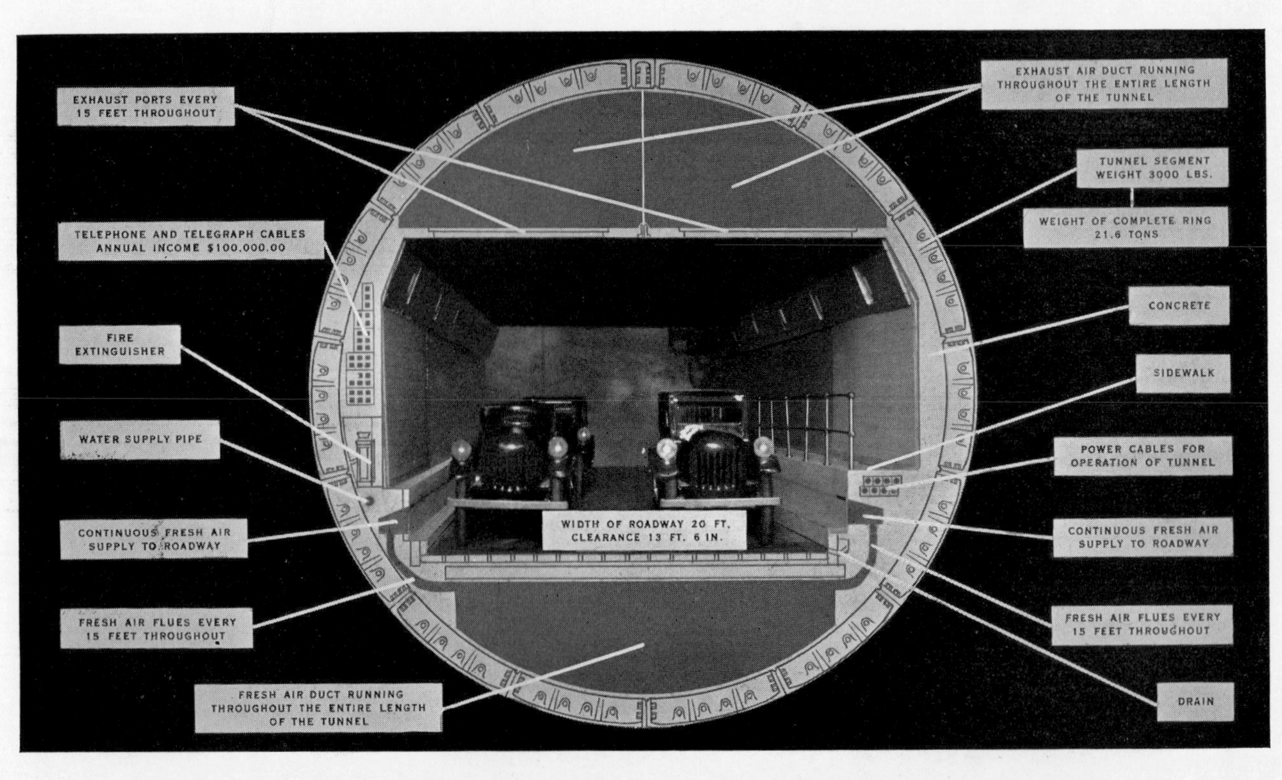

MODEL OF THE HOLLAND TUNNEL SHOWING MANY OF THE HIDDEN DETAILS

displaced compressed silt to enter the tunnel on each shove.

We stood watching the big burly men as they shoveled the debris into the cars that carried it out through the lower air chambers. Not particularly envious of them at such hard labor, we listened only half-heartedly to our guide until he remarked that the automobiles we had seen parked at the entrance belonged to these very "sand-hogs"; that they made high wages and worked short hours. There are laws forbidding their working in compressed air for more than two hours at a time, for health reasons. Law likewise requires the company employing the men to furnish hot showers and hot coffee for them when they come out.

From the digging, we turned to watch the erector; two men tugging at a mammoth wrench tightening the bolts; the grouting machine as it forced its mixture with pressure beyond the segments to form a concrete shell for the whole tube; and then to discuss the miracle that prevented the Hudson itself from pouring in on us in one deluge. There we stood with only a few feet of sand and gravel between us and the river.

"Chief" Holland and the rest of the engineers chatted with us as casually as if it were a game of tiddle-de-winks they were explaining, instead of an achievement that even seeing defied believing. We picked up bits of rock for souvenirs and continued gasping when one of our hosts turned questioner. He asked if we could whistle.

Assuring him that whistling did not stump the modern girl, we inquired his preference as to a tune. He consulted the other men, and after much deliberation proposed to give us a big party on the condition that we whistle "Yankee Doodle" — all five verses. With one accord lips were puckered and cheeks distended. Our chagrin was only equaled by the laughter of our tormentors as we puffed and blew in vain. The party was given for effort and not for the results obtained against twenty-nine pounds of pressure.

In quitting the compressed air it was necessary to put on fleece-lined coats to prevent catching cold. We retraced our steps through the man-lock, where the pressure was reduced gradually back through the tube, and insisted on the law requirement of hot coffee on signing off.

VIII

THE problem of ventilation of the Holland Tunnel was unlike any heretofore solved, both in character and magnitude. The only existing vehicular tunnels even approximately comparable to the Holland Tunnel are the Blackwall and Rotherhithe Tunnels under the Thames at London.

The Blackwall, opened for traffic in 1897, has an under-river length of 1221 feet between shafts. It consists of a single tube 27 feet in diameter with a roadway accommodating one line of traffic in each direction and two side-walks. Traffic counts in 1920 showed that the maximum number of motor vehicles using the tunnel was less than 100 per hour.

The Rotherhithe is 30 feet in diameter, similar to the Blackwall in traffic facilities, with an under-river length between shafts of 1570 feet. Both of these tunnels are ventilated by the natural movement of air through the shafts and portals. The Holland Tunnel, with a total length of 9250 feet, an under-river length of 5480 feet, and a capacity of 1900 vehicles per hour in each direction, or 46,000 per day, obviously required something more than natural ventilation. To this end the ventilation of the tunnel was studied under three heads:

1. The amount and composition of exhaust gases from motor vehicles.
2. The dilution necessary to render the exhaust gases harmless.
3. The method and equipment necessary for adequate ventilation.

The impurities in the atmosphere of a tunnel used by motor vehicles are the product of the combustion of gasoline. If complete combustion occurred, the carbon content in the gasoline would be in the form of carbon dioxide, which can be tolerated in considerable quantity without injurious effects. In a gasoline engine, however, complete combustion seldom, if ever, takes place. The exhaust gases contain varying amounts of carbon monoxide, depending on such variable factors as the quality of the gasoline, conditions of carburetion, etc.

Carbon monoxide is a highly poisonous gas, injurious to health in minute quantities if breathed for a long time, and if present in large quantities is injurious even when breathed for a short time. Ventilation requirements are determined by the quantity of this gas in exhaust gases. If sufficient fresh air is supplied to reduce this gas to a safe percentage, other gases and impurities, such as carbon dioxide, methane, and smoke, will also be diluted sufficiently. The first consideration, therefore, was to determine the amount of carbon monoxide that would be liberated in the tunnel.

Investigations were carried out at the Bureau of Mines Experiment Station at Pittsburgh. The schedule called for the testing of passenger cars and trucks of various makes and capacities. The tests were made with car loaded and light, standing with engine racing and idling, accelerating from rest on level grade and on maximum grade, running at three, six, ten, and fifteen miles per hour on level and up and down a grade of 3½%, corresponding to the maximum tunnel grade. A total of 101 cars were tested. Gas samples were taken directly from

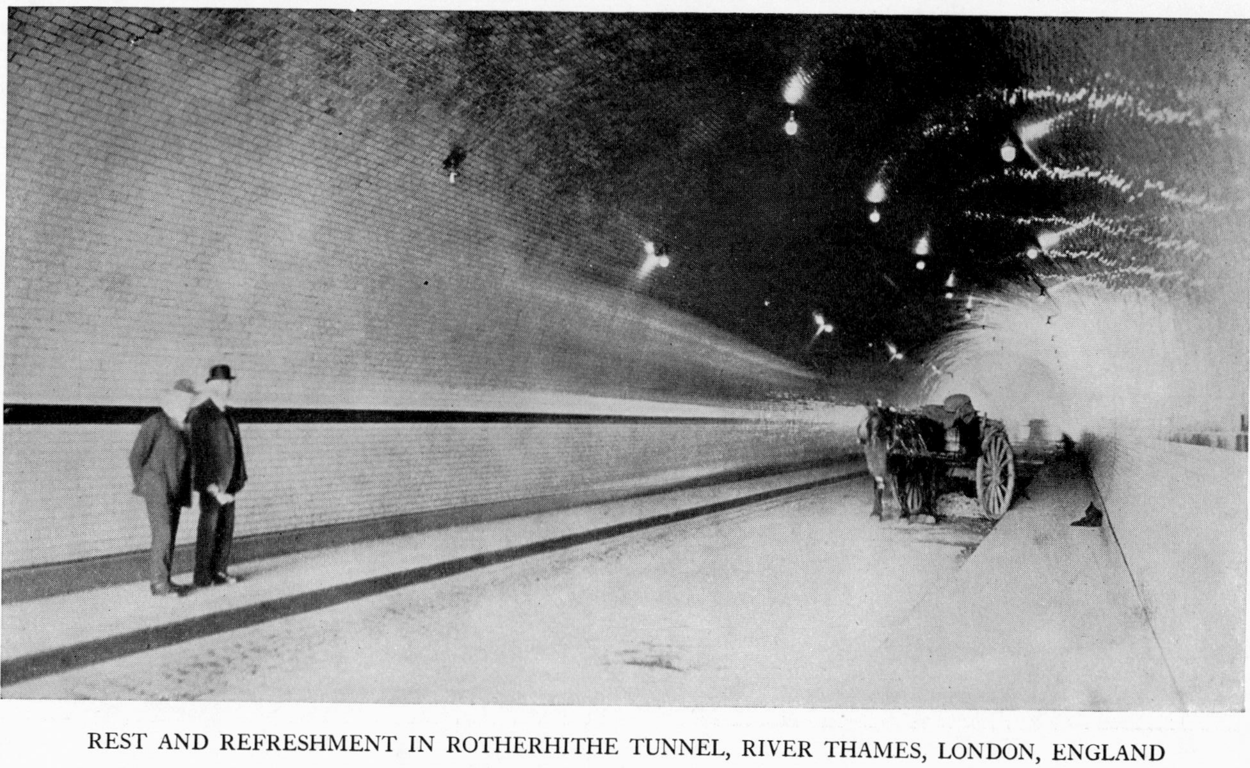

REST AND REFRESHMENT IN ROTHERHITHE TUNNEL, RIVER THAMES, LONDON, ENGLAND

HEAVY TRAFFIC ON THE BLACKWALL TUNNEL, RIVER THAMES, LONDON, ENGLAND

the exhaust pipe throughout the entire duration of the test.

In general, the results showed that the exhaust gases contained about 6.8% carbon monoxide and 8.4% carbon dioxide, developing only 67% of the heat value of the gasoline. About one-third of the gasoline fuel was wasted through incomplete combustion.

Experiments to determine the proper dilution to render the exhaust gases harmless were conducted at the Bureau of Mines Experiment Station at Yale. They were performed in a gas-tight chamber of 226 cubic feet capacity. Members of the staff spent periods of one hour in air containing amounts of carbon monoxide varying from two to ten parts in 10,000. In addition, tests were performed in a chamber of 12,000 cubic feet with an automobile engine exhausting into the chamber. The duration of all tests was one hour, whereas the length of time required to travel through the tunnel at a speed of only three miles per hour is but 31 minutes.

The results of the test showed that when an automobile engine is running properly, the exhaust contains no substance that is injurious to any appreciable extent except carbon monoxide. Gasoline engines with cylinders missing, or when cold, over-supplied with oil or gasoline, or smoking from any cause, may throw off disagreeable vapors irritating to the eyes and nauseating to some persons.

The physiological effects of carbon monoxide are wholly due to the union of this gas with the hemoglobin of the blood. To the extent that hemoglobin is combined with carbon monoxide, it is by that amount incapable of transporting oxygen to the body. This combination of carbon monoxide with the hemoglobin is reversible, so that when a person returns to fresh air the carbon monoxide is gradually eliminated.

Of all physical signs and tests of carbon monoxide poisoning, headache proved the most definite and reliable. Concentrations of gas too weak or periods of exposure too short to induce a headache are to be considered harmless. No one had this symptom to an appreciable degree after a period of one hour in the chamber with four parts of carbon monoxide. With six parts the effect was usually very slight, while with eight parts there was decided discomfort for some hours.

Hence a uniform concentration of four parts carbon monoxide in 10,000 of air is designed to afford not only complete safety, but also comfort and freedom from disagreeable effects.

IX

BY the longitudinal method of ventilation, the entire tunnel would be utilized as a duct for conveying air through the tunnel. Sufficient air would be supplied through blower fans near one portal and would enter the tunnel through a nozzle or nozzles at a velocity sufficient to force it through its entire length.

If in a 29-foot tunnel the air were introduced into the north tube near one portal through a nozzle having a cross-sectional area of 74 square feet, and were exhausted through the opposite portal, the air would have a nozzle velocity of about 282 miles per hour. This would produce a velocity of 72 miles per hour at points where the roadway was occupied by a pleasure car and a truck abreast, or a velocity of 51 miles per hour where there were no vehicles. Such air velocities would be prohibitive in a vehicular tunnel, and the power required to handle the air would be excessive.

In the distributive method of ventilation adopted for the Holland Tunnel, the air is introduced into and exhausted from the tunnel through a number of openings at frequent intervals leading from the tunnel roadway. By this method fresh air is supplied at all points throughout the tunnel. The air at any point can be controlled. There is no discomfort or danger from high-velocity air currents. The ventilation is not affected by traffic or the direction of the wind. Exhaust gases are quickly diluted and removed.

The space above and below the tunnel roadway is ideally suitable for air ducts. Fresh air, supplied by blower fans at the shafts, is discharged from the main duct under the roadway through adjustable openings into continuous expansion chambers on each side, thence through a continuous slot into the roadway. The air remains in the

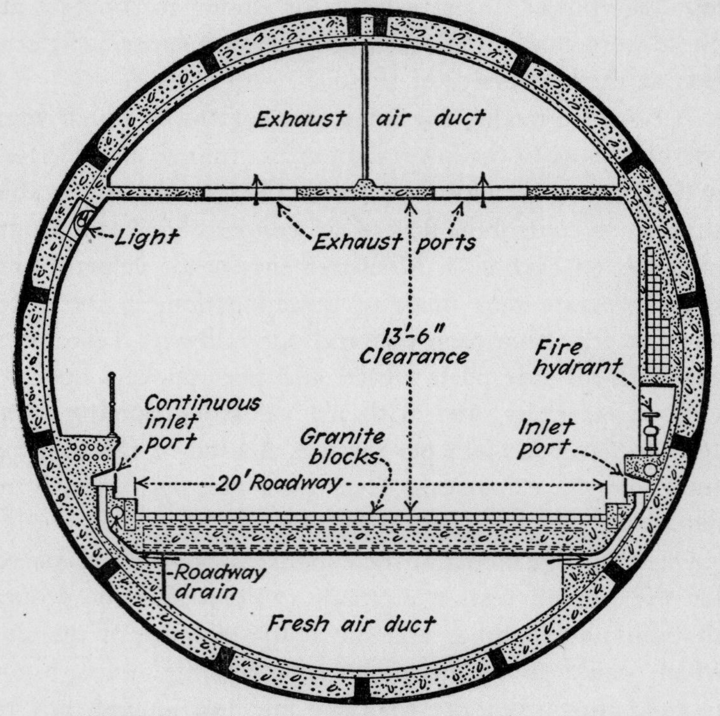

CROSS SECTION — ONE TUBE OF HOLLAND TUNNEL

tunnel an average of one and one-half minutes as it slowly ascends to the ceiling.

Exhaust fans located in the same buildings with the blower fans draw the vitiated air through ports in the ceiling and thence through the upper duct above the roadway, delivering it through stacks to the outer atmosphere.

Experiments to determine the coefficient of friction for flow of air in concrete ducts, to verify formulæ used in computing the power required for moving air through a duct from which air is taken off at intervals, and to determine the power losses in bends or elbows in concrete air ducts were conducted at the engineering experiment station at the University of Illinois.

A concrete model, the linear dimensions of which were one-half those of the lower duct of the tunnel, and 300 feet in length, was used for direct tests. Outlets with adjustable shutters to control the flow of air were provided at uniform intervals on each side. Measurements of air velocity and static pressure were made at three locations in the duct, one five feet from each end and one midway. Tests were run with all side ports closed and port pockets open at various intervals, and with air velocities ranging from 1000 feet to 6000 feet per minute. A total of 186 blowing tests and 17 exhausting tests were run from which to determine the coefficient of friction.

On a full-size model of the expansion chamber proposed for the tunnel, tests were made to determine the proper shape of the chamber and the shape and size of the slot which would give a direction of air flow high enough not to raise dust from the roadway and low enough not to short circuit the fresh air to the inlets into the vitiated air duct over the roadway. These experiments also gave the minimum static pressure required to discharge the requisite quantities of air through the slots at different locations in the tunnel. A total of 112 tests were made on various shapes of expansion chambers and various widths of slot under the several conditions to be met in the tunnel.

Experiments on elbows were made in two parts: on galvanized iron single and compound elbows constructed to one-tenth the interior dimensions of the elbows to be used in the tunnel, and on concrete compound elbows to one-half the interior dimensions of those planned for the tunnel ducts.

To verify under tunnel conditions the amount of carbon monoxide produced by automobiles and the physiological effect of exhaust gases, an experimental tunnel was constructed in the workings of a coal mine at Bruceton, Pa. It was located about 1000 feet from the entrance to the mine and about 135 feet from the surface. The tunnel had a driveway 8 feet by 9 feet wide, with continuous air ducts above the ceiling and below the roadway. It was oval in plan, with a major axis of approximately 135 feet and a minor axis of approximately 110 feet, giving a roadway length of 400 feet.

Air for the test was supplied by the mine fan, belt-connected to a steam engine and operated outside the mines. The fan operated normally exhausting, giving upward ventilation in the tunnel. Downward ventilation was accomplished by reversing the direction of the air currents through the reversible housing of the fan, which then operated as a blower.

In the upward ventilation system, air entered the duct under the roadway, passed through adjustable port openings into the continuous expansion chambers on either side of the roadway, thence into the driveway. In the downward system, air was delivered to the duct in the ceiling, thence through the ports into the upper expansion chambers from which it entered the roadway.

EAST BLOWER AIR DUCT
In Land Ventilation Building, New York City, showing curved back and vanes

EAST BLOWER AIR DUCT
Land Ventilation Building, New York City

FRESH-AIR DUCT IN SOUTH TUNNEL, N. J. SIDE
Showing the beginning of the transition from its position under the roadway to its position alongside the tunnel

TILE AND BRONZE WORK
(Left to right) Bronze door to relay niche with telephone and fire alarm boxes on each side; tiled refuge niche with fresh-air outlet on each side, two fire extinguisher niches; tiled opening to mid-river sump

A total of seventeen tests were run with cars varying in number from 1 to 8, with concentrations of carbon monoxide in the driveway from 0.5 to 9.4 in 10,000 parts of air, at various temperatures and humidities, and various methods of transverse ventilation. The tests verified the earlier conclusions, and demonstrated that with upward ventilation the exhaust gases crossed the breathing plane of persons in the tunnel but once, while with downward ventilation they crossed this plane twice. There was also a lower concentration of carbon monoxide with upward than with downward ventilation.

X

VALUABLE and necessary as were the experiments required to determine the various factors involved in the problem of adequate ventilation for the Holland Tunnel, the data resulting from these preliminary investigations had to be crystallized into tangible units of ventilating equipment.

These are the eighty-four giant Sturtevant Silentvane Fans which are the very lungs of the tunnel. Without such fans blowing in fresh air and exhausting the vitiated air the tunnel could not be made to function.

Mr. B. F. Sturtevant, the founder of the company which constructed the fans, was a Maine shoemaker of inventive genius. He had devised a machine to shave a ribbon of wood from a log, form it into pegs, and drive them into shoes. This process, however, created a dust which bothered his workmen. Accordingly, he next constructed a fan which performed as an exhauster and removed the dust. Thus the first fan was created.

Concentrating on this latter invention, he established what grew into the B. F. Sturtevant Company, with its great plants and offices, research laboratories and corps of engineers, and its wide variety of products in the field of fans, blowers, and allied air-moving equipment.

The Sturtevant Silentvane Fan is an outstanding achievement, since it has demonstrated under a variety of tests efficiencies greater than any other type of centrifugal fan. For the work of ventilating the Holland Tunnel it showed efficiencies varying from 15% to 20% higher

LAND VENTILATION BUILDING
West side of Washington St., Canal to Spring Sts., New York City

RIVER VENTILATION BUILDING

Pierhead line between piers 34 and 35, North River, New York City

than any other fan that could have been used for the purpose, and by reducing the amount of power required, the investment in motors was correspondingly less. Its selection was therefore inevitable.

The Sturtevant Silentvane Fans are installed in the ventilation buildings, of which there are two on each side of the river, one at the pierhead line and the other inland. Each land shaft ventilates four sections of tunnel, — the adjoining portal sections of each tube, the whole intermediate section to the pierhead shaft where traffic is on a downgrade, and one-half of the parallel section where it is on an upgrade. The buildings over these shafts contain four independent sets of blower and exhaust fans. The pierhead shafts ventilate three sections of tunnel, — one-half of each of the 3400-foot river sections and one-half of the intermediate section where traffic is on the upgrade. In all there are 14 sets of blowers and 14 sets of exhaust fans. Dividing the upgrade sections of the tunnels into three parts gives added ventilation where the greatest amount of carbon monoxide is expected.

There are 28 ducts, 14 blower and 14 exhaust, connecting the various sections of the tunnels with the ventilating buildings. Each duct is equipped with three fans, two of which, when operated together, will supply the maximum quantity of air required. Their capacities range from 81,000 to 227,000 cubic feet per minute and they operate at static pressures varying from 0.6 to 3.75 inches of water. This range in pressure and capacity is due to the great difference in length of tunnel ventilated by different sets, those at the outside of the pierhead shafts having 1700 feet to serve while the inside fans have only 700 or 800 feet.

These fans, during an hour of heavy traffic, will handle 84,000 tons of air, or 1400 tons per minute. They provide for changing the air in the tunnel 42 times per hour.

The fans are of the backward curved-blade type. Under different conditions, one, two, or three fans may be operated on one tunnel duct at any one time. By the use of the Sturtevant Silentvane, assurance is given that they will operate satisfactorily when run in parallel without the danger of any one fan assuming more than its share of the load and overloading the motor. They will also maintain satisfactory efficiency for any stage of loading from 35% to full load.

They are electrically driven by wound-rotor motors with resistance in the circuit to make it possible to run them at variable speeds. The combined capacities of the motors is approximately 6000 horse power, two-thirds of which will be in operation at times of maximum load and one-third in reserve. Chain drives are to be used to make possible speed adjustments or changes in the motors as well as on account of the space limitations in the ventilating buildings.

The placing of the fans is varied to suit the local conditions in the individual buildings. Generally, the exhaust ducts are at the corners of the buildings and supply ducts are in the central portion. Consequently the compartments containing the exhaust fans are located near the corners under the exhaust stacks, leaving the central portions of the fan floors free for intake fans, and the central section of each outer wall for the air intakes. The intakes are made sufficiently large to give low velocities through the louvres.

SPECIAL APPARATUS ERECTED AT HYDE PARK PLANT OF B. F. STURTEVANT COMPANY
Used in testing Sturtevant Silentvane Fans for the Holland Tunnel

STURTEVANT SILENTVANE FAN WHEELS FOR THE HOLLAND TUNNEL

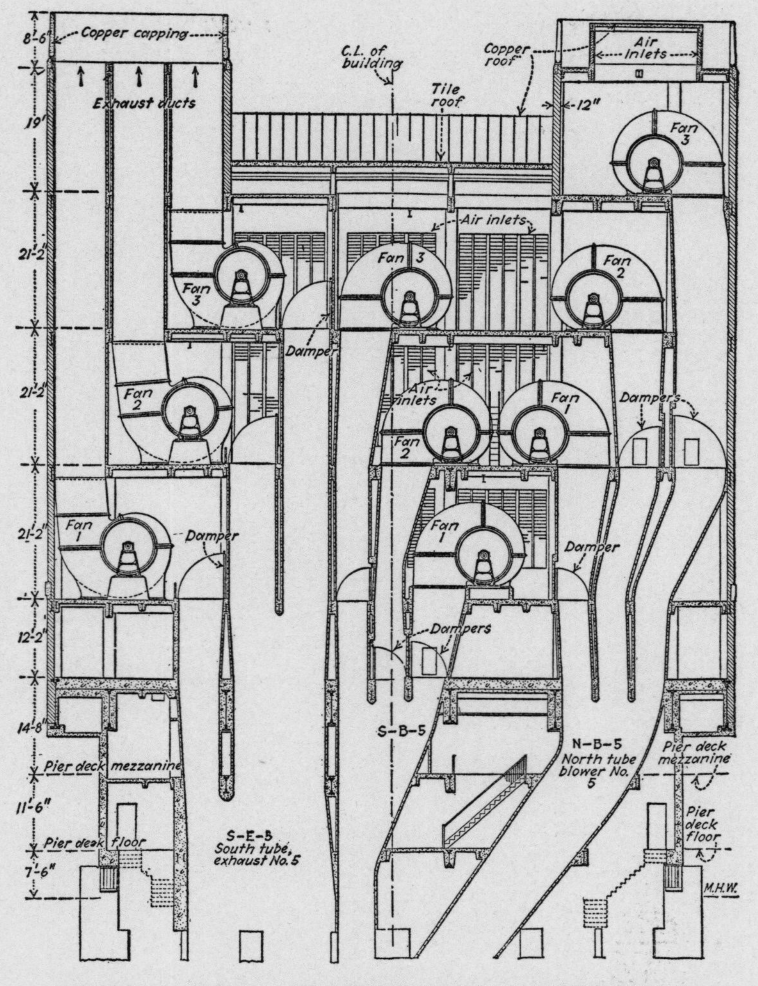

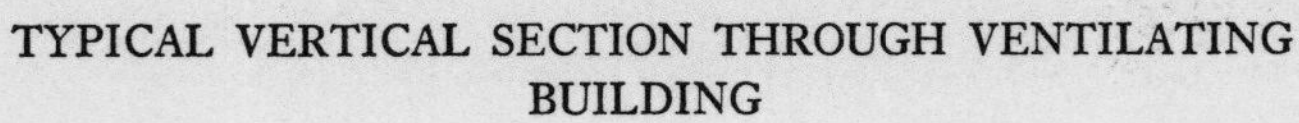
TYPICAL VERTICAL SECTION THROUGH VENTILATING BUILDING

The louvre blades are made of heavy wire glass to give light to the interior of the buildings as they take up most of the space otherwise available for windows. Heavy bronze screens protect them and also serve to keep out birds.

The arrangement whereby fresh air is drawn in through louvres high up on the sides of the buildings and exhaust air is forced out through stacks which extend 20 feet above the roof insures a complete separation of fresh and vitiated air.

The intake fans and their motors are situated in the open portions of the fan floors where they are accessible. The exhaust fans are, of necessity, inside of chambers at the top of the ducts. Their motors, however, are out on the main floor, the drive shafts being run in to the fans through close-fitting collars in the side plates of the duct. Access to the fans is provided through air locks equipped with airtight doors which can be opened against the unequal pressure by wedge latches which force the doors open sufficiently to break the seal.

Each duct is equipped with a damper which may be closed when the fan is shut down so that air from the other fans will not be short-circuited through the idle fan. These dampers are motor operated from the control room and are equipped with limit switches.

An unusually flexible system of power supply has been worked out based on the facts that all the motors are in groups of three, also that the maximum power equipments are less than the capacity of the minimum size power cables installed by the local companies. Three cables from the New York side and three from the New Jersey side are run to the bus bars in each ventilating building, thus giving one motor in each set a separate cable connection

ONE OF THE 84 STURTEVANT SILENTVANE FANS
Which are the lungs of the Holland Tunnel

EXHAUST FAN UNIT IN N. J. LAND VENTILATION BUILDING

Showing typical arrangement of exhaust fan, motor, chain casing, resistors, control cabinet, and local control box to power supply on each side of the river. Interconnection at the bus bars makes it possible to cut in any or all motors on each cable. Thus connected, each motor may be supplied with power by six independent cables, each capable of carrying the entire tunnel load; and, as there are at least two independent sources of power at each end of the tunnel, continuity of power supply is absolutely assured.

As the transformers are located in the ventilating buildings where smoke from an oil fire might be drawn into the ventilating system, air-cooled instead of oil-cooled transformers are used.

Each fan is provided with a control switch at the motor for emergency or repair use. Further local control is provided at the switchboard in each ventilating building, and complete operating control is provided at the main switchboard in the administration building where, by a system of signal lights, it will be possible, at all times, to tell what motors are in operation.

Air from the intake fans is forced down into the longitudinal duct under the roadway of the tunnel. From there it is fed through flues 10 to 15 feet apart into a continuous expansion chamber above the curb line at each side of the roadway, the flow of air into this chamber being controlled by adjustable slides over the flue openings. The outer side of the expansion chamber is a copper-steel plate which can be adjusted to give an opening of widths varying from ¾ inches to 1¾ inches through which fresh air flows into the tunnel.

Vitiated air is drawn off through openings through the ceiling into the exhaust ducts. These openings are spaced 10 to 15 feet apart and are from 3 to 6 feet long. They, also, are provided with slides by which the opening can be adjusted to meet the local requirements for air circulation.

By this arrangement of supply and exhaust ports, fresh air supplied to the roadway mixes with the warmer gases and rises to the ceiling where the exhaust ports are located.

There will be no longitudinal movement of air in the tunnels except that induced by the movement of vehicles, nor will there be any objectionable winds such as would be created by longitudinal ventilation. Tests made with smoke bombs showed that even large quantities of smoke will not spread far from the point of origin, but will rise quickly to the ceiling and be taken out. Similarly, in case of a fire the hot gases will rise to the ceiling, where they will be drawn off. There will not be the same danger of spreading the fire from car to car as there would be with longitudinal ventilation.

As part of the studies for the ventilating equipment numerous tests in relation to fire were made, both in the test tunnel at Bruceton and at the laboratories of manufacturers of fire-fighting equipment. These tests included the burning of an automobile drenched with gasoline and with gasoline spilling from a hole in the tank on the car to determine how quickly such a fire could be put out with the hand extinguishers to be placed in the tunnel.

As a check upon the air conditions in the tunnel, automatic carbon monoxide recording devices are installed in each exhaust duct which will make a continuous analysis of the gases and record it graphically in the control room of the administration building in New York. There, by observing the chart, the operator can increase or decrease the fresh-air supply as traffic conditions change in the tunnel.

THE HOLLAND TUNNEL COMPLETED
Seven years of study, research and labor

CONDENSATION IN NORTH TUNNEL

View showing dry condition of roadway east of air duct bulkhead where fans were in operation, and wet condition of roadway west of air duct bulkhead where fans were not in operation

XI

THE Holland Tunnel well illustrates the modern attitude of service to the community at large that should be a normal function of every great business. The ventilation of the tunnel presented an entirely new problem. The tunnel engineers took an enlightened view of the requirements of the work, realized that there was ample glory for all concerned, and freely availed themselves of the experience and services of manufacturers of ventilating equipment, which service was equally freely rendered. Without this coöperation it is hardly probable that the problem would have been solved with so much certainty and with so few false steps.

The B. F. Sturtevant Company put its research department, with its director, Mr. H. F. Hagen, at the service of the tunnel engineers. This service was exactly that of a well-equipped consulting engineering company, and was carried out without thought of commercial return.

A difference of opinion arose as to the type of fan best suited for ventilating the tunnels. This question was definitely settled in the laboratory of the company in tests made by the engineers of the tunnel and of the company. A further problem arose in that the resistances to the flow of air which would be encountered in the actual installation were entirely frictional. There was a great dearth of information about the frictional resistances of ducts, and the company's research department was able to outline a procedure for the determination of the factors necessary for the solution of this extremely important point. These tests were later very ably carried out at the engineering experimental station at the University of Illinois, as previously mentioned.

The selection of the proper type of fans to be used and the determination of the resistances against which they would operate were the two most important requirements of this unprecedented ventilation problem. In addition, through the extended experience of the company's research department, proper methods for installing the equipment were determined, and suitable motors for driving the fans and suitable connections to ducts were selected, all of which assured the final success of the installation as a whole.

The ideal co-operation that existed at all times between the tunnel engineers and the engineers of the company is an example of the broadmindedness and large ability that should exist in business. During the vital preliminaries it was clearly understood that no commercial advantage was to accrue to the company. The company and its engineers felt that, as the largest manufacturers of ventilating equipment in the world, they were directly concerned with the success of the greatest ventilation project in the world. It was a matter of industrial pride on the part of the company and its engineers to do all they could to insure its final success.

In the final bidding the company proved its right to be considered a leader in the industry not only by quoting by far the lowest price but also by showing a total power consumption of 15% less than its nearest competitor.

The operation of the ventilating equipment in the Holland Tunnel has been a source of gratification to the

Photo by Underwood and Underwood

OLE SINGSTAD, CHIEF ENGINEER

Under whose direction the Holland Tunnel was brought to successful completion

MODEL OF ENTRANCE TO TUNNEL, NEW YORK CITY
Looking north-northwest across entrance plaza which comprises north half of block between Broome and Watts Streets

MODEL OF EXIT FROM TUNNEL, NEW YORK CITY
Looking northwest along Canal Street

company and its engineers and to the tunnel engineers. The preliminary work was planned and carried out with great exactitude. The results secured have been wholly those desired and have been obtained without the aid of the unreasonable allowances so frequently used in work planned less skillfully.

That the construction of the Holland Tunnel was no easy task is evidenced by the great increase in both time and money required for its completion. The original plans called for an expenditure of approximately $28,000,000 and for completion in 1924, or three and one-half years. Actual expenditures have run 50% greater, and as this is written, the opening will not be until the fall of 1927.

Yet this is not surprising. Although the shield method of construction has been described in this story as if it were a relatively simple operation, many difficulties had to be overcome in bringing the work to a successful conclusion. The proceedings involved in the taking of real property at entrances and exits, changes in the grades of streets, the closing of a portion of 11th Street in Jersey City, negotiations with the railroads at the Jersey City end for the acquisition of parts of the railroad yards, all took time. It was not always easy to harmonize the views of the State Commissions. Alterations necessarily had to be made in the preliminary plans as further information resulted from investigation and experience.

That the undertaking cost the lives of its first two chief engineers — not from accident, but from the drain on their vital energy — is perhaps the most striking evidence of the magnitude of the undertaking.

Doubtless other tunnels under the Hudson will be built.

Other problems in successful ventilation will be solved. The Sturtevant Silentvane Fan will be put to other uses of equal importance to humanity. But for many years to come the Holland Tunnel will remain one of the modern wonders of the world — a triumph in the science of ventilation.

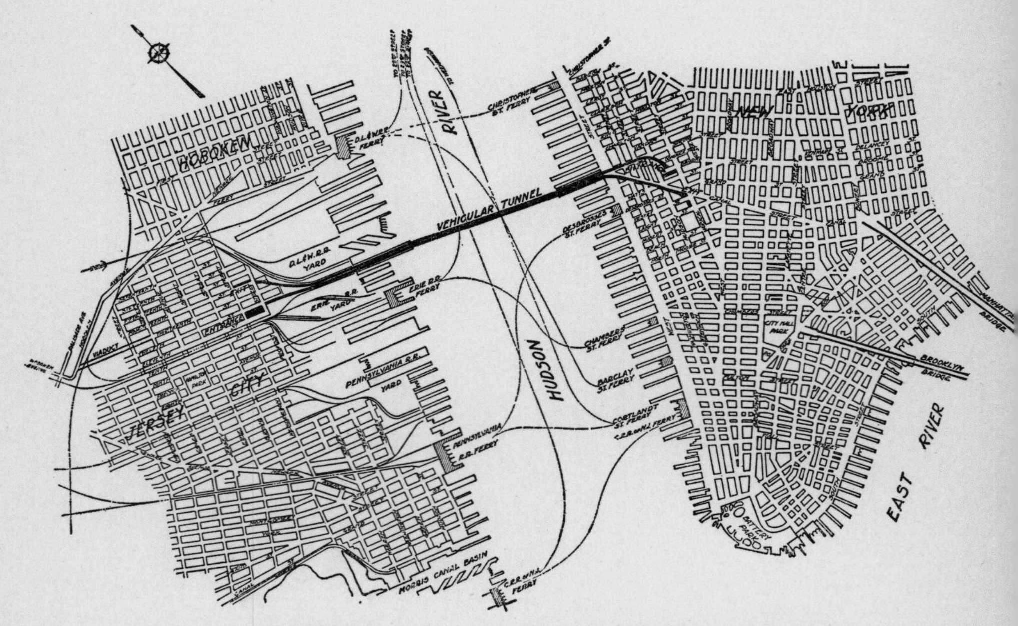

LOCATION PLAN OF HOLLAND VEHICULAR TUNNEL